GRIMMY AND THE TEMPLE OF GROOM

by Mike Peters

A TRUMPET CLUB SPECIAL EDITION

Published by The Trumpet Club
1540 Broadway, New York, New York 10036

GRIMMY AND THE TEMPLE OF GROOM and MOTHER GOOSE &
GRIMM characters copyright: TM and © 1992 Grimmy, Inc. Comic
strips distributed by Tribune Media Services. Licensed by MGM L&M.

ISBN 0-440-83049-4

This edition published by arrangement with Funk & Wagnalls Corp.
Printed in the United States of America
September 1993

10 9 8 7 6 5 4 3 2 1

CWO

GRIMMY
AND THE
TEMPLE
OF GROOM

Special thanks to Chris Browne for coming up with the title.

Panel 1: OH, BOY... MAPS, CLOTHES, SUITCASE... LOOKS LIKE SOMEONE IS GOING ON A TRIP.

Panel 2: GRIMMY, I'M GOING TO VISIT MY SISTER IN ST. LOUIS. I'LL BE GONE FOR A WEEK.

Panel 3: NO PROBLEM... I'LL GUARD THE HOUSE WITH MY LIFE..... WHERE'S THE CHANNEL CHANGER?

Panel 4: NO, GRIMMY, I'M TAKING YOU TO THE HAPPY ACRES DOG KENNEL... TAMMY BAKKER'S HOG RENTAL?

Panel 5: C'MON, GRIMMY... YOU'RE JUST GOING TO THE DOG KENNEL FOR A WEEK. NO, NO

Panel 6: IF YOU'RE GOING TO FIGHT LIKE THIS, I'M GOING TO HAVE TO TAKE YOU THERE IN A CAGE!!

Panel 7: SHE CAN'T LOCK ME UP LIKE THIS, CAN SHE? IS THIS LEGAL? NO TRIAL, NO JUDGE, NO JURY... BUT HERE I AM...

Panel 8: ...THE BIRD DOG OF ALCATRAZ.

Panel 9: HELLO, GRIMMY... WELCOME TO HAPPY ACRES DOG KENNEL... I HEAR YOU'RE A LITTLE HIGH STRUNG SINCE THIS IS YOUR FIRST TIME HERE.

Panel 10: WELL, DON'T BE NERVOUS, BOY... COM'ON, COM'ON, COME OUT OF THE CAGE, COM'ON JUMP, JUMP ...COM'ON, GRIMMY... JUMP, JUMP...

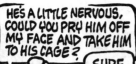

Panel 1: MISS HARTWORM, THIS IS GRIMMY'S FIRST DAY AT HAPPY ACRES DOG KENNEL,

Panel 2: HE'S A LITTLE NERVOUS, COULD YOU PRY HIM OFF MY FACE AND TAKE HIM TO HIS CAGE? — SURE,

Panel 3: I THINK HE LIKES YOU.

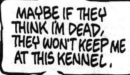

Panel 4: I'VE GOT AN IDEA.

Panel 5: MAYBE IF THEY THINK I'M DEAD, THEY WON'T KEEP ME AT THIS KENNEL.

Panel 6: OH, DEAR...THAT POOR LITTLE DOG IS DEAD. I GUESS WE'LL HAVE TO CREMATE HIM.

Panel 7: THERE'S NO BUSINESS LIKE SHOW BUSINESS.... TAP TAP TAP TAP TAP

Panel 8: HERE I AM....ALL ALONE....LOCKED UP BEHIND BARS...

Panel 9: LIVING ON BREAD AND WATER AND SLEEPING ON A COLD FLOOR....

Panel 10: WHY DO I HAVE THIS SUDDEN URGE TO PLAY A HARMONICA?

DOWN AND OUT ON BEVERLY SILLS

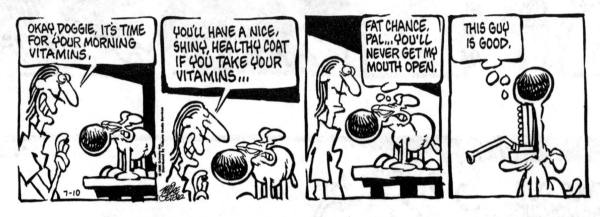

Mother Goose & GRIMM

ROCKY THE LYING SQUIRREL

CONAN THE CENTURION

GEEZ...WHAT A TERRIBLE PICTURE OF YOU...

DRIVER'S LICENSE OF DORIAN GRAY

MEAL TIME IS SO MUCH MORE ENJOYABLE....

"WHEN YOU DON'T HAVE TO COME UP FOR AIR.

© 1988 Tribune Media Services, Inc.
All Rights Reserved

10-10

YOU'RE FEEDING HIM TOO MUCH FIBER.

© 1988 Tribune Media Services, Inc.
All Rights Reserved

11-23

SHAKE, GRIMMY, SHAKE, SHAKE....

ZZIITTT

I SHOULD'VE TOLD HER ABOUT THE JOY BUZZER.

© 1988 Tribune Media Services, Inc.
All Rights Reserved

10-13

PLANET OF THE HOMO SAPIENS

PLANE

AND FINALLY THE CHOICE CAME DOWN TO CINDERELLA AND HER SISTER MOZZARELLA.

ROBIN HOOD AND LITTLE JOHN

FLEAS AT GOLF

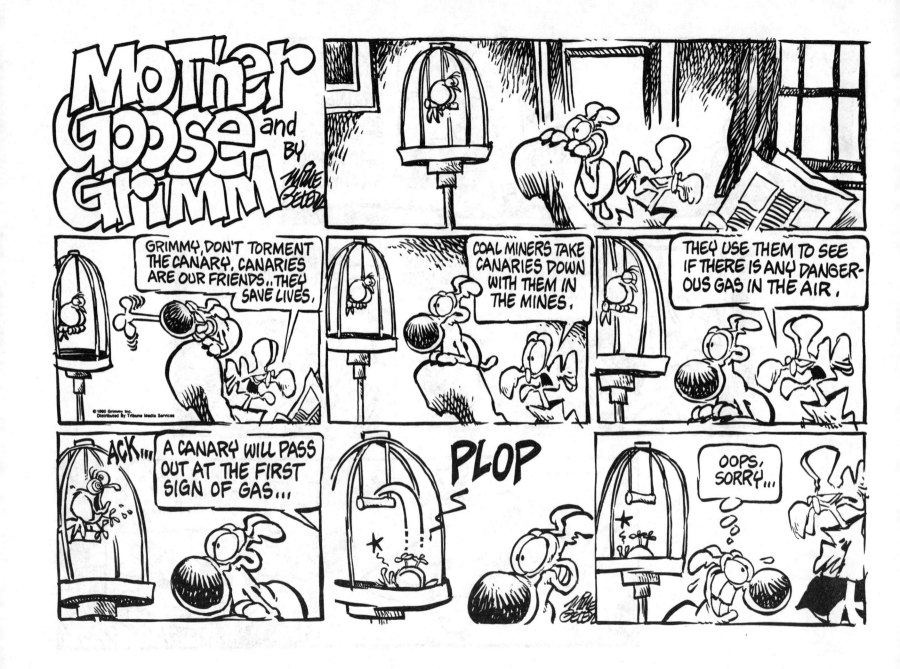

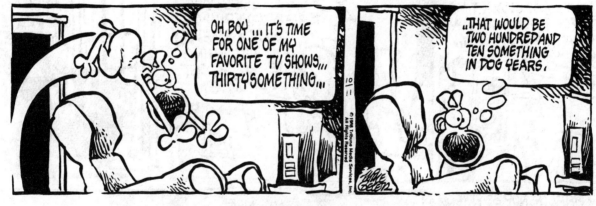

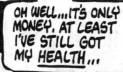

I CAN'T BELIEVE THAT DIRTY DOG ATE MY FORTUNE....I'M OUT 35 MILLION DOLLARS.

OH WELL...IT'S ONLY MONEY. AT LEAST I'VE STILL GOT MY HEALTH...

"AND A ROOF OVER MY HEAD AND ENOUGH FOOD TO LIVE ON...

I'M STARTING TO SOUND LIKE IVANA TRUMP.

3-22

LOOK, THIS PAPER I WROTE MY LOTTERY NUMBER ON WAS UPSIDE DOWN !!!

SO...WHAT I THOUGHT WAS MY WINNING NUMBER 1899618011 WAS ONLY 1108196681.

SO, I GUESS I DON'T NEED THAT LOTTERY STUB THAT GRIMMY SWALLOWED, AFTER ALL...

"...YOU CAN STOP NOW, GRIMMY.

MUNCH GULP

FIBER BRAN PRUNES

3-23

WEIGHT AND FORTUNE

YOU'VE GAINED WEIGHT AND LOST A FORTUNE.

3/24

mother Goose and Grimm

BY MIKE PETERS

LOBO THE ARCTIC WOLF USES HIS ACUTE SENSE OF SMELL TO LOCATE A BEAR'S CAVE.

SLOWLY, LOBO CRAWLS TOWARD THE LARGE, HIBERNATING BEAR.

INCH BY INCH, LOBO GETS WITHIN STRIKING DISTANCE.

CHOMP YAH

GRIMMY!

YOU'VE GOT TO STOP IMAGINING THAT YOU'RE A WOLF... DO YOU UNDERSTAND? YOU'RE NOT A WOLF.

OKAY, I WON'T BE A WOLF, I WON'T BE A WOLF...

DUM DUM, DUM DUM,

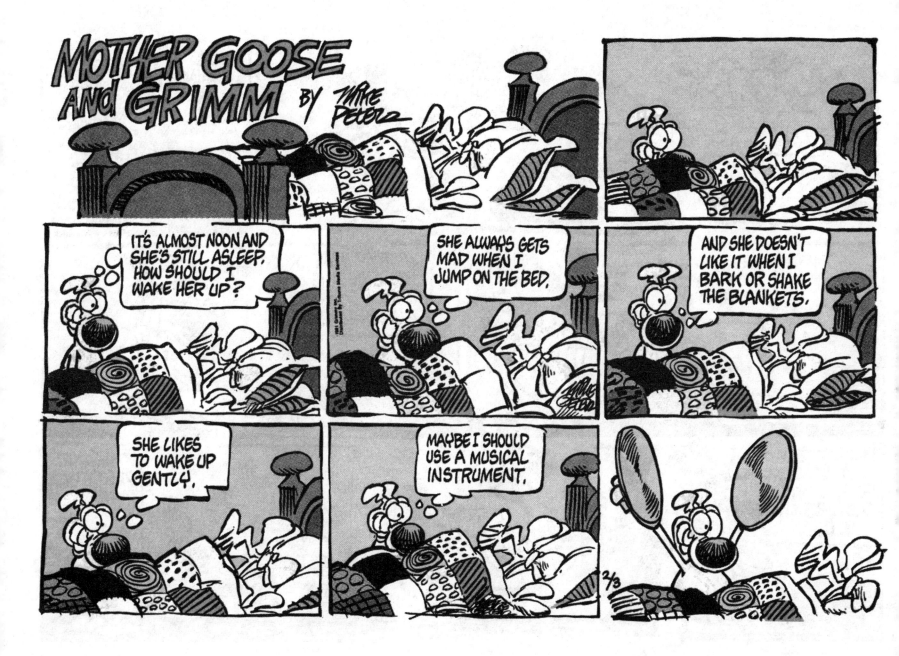

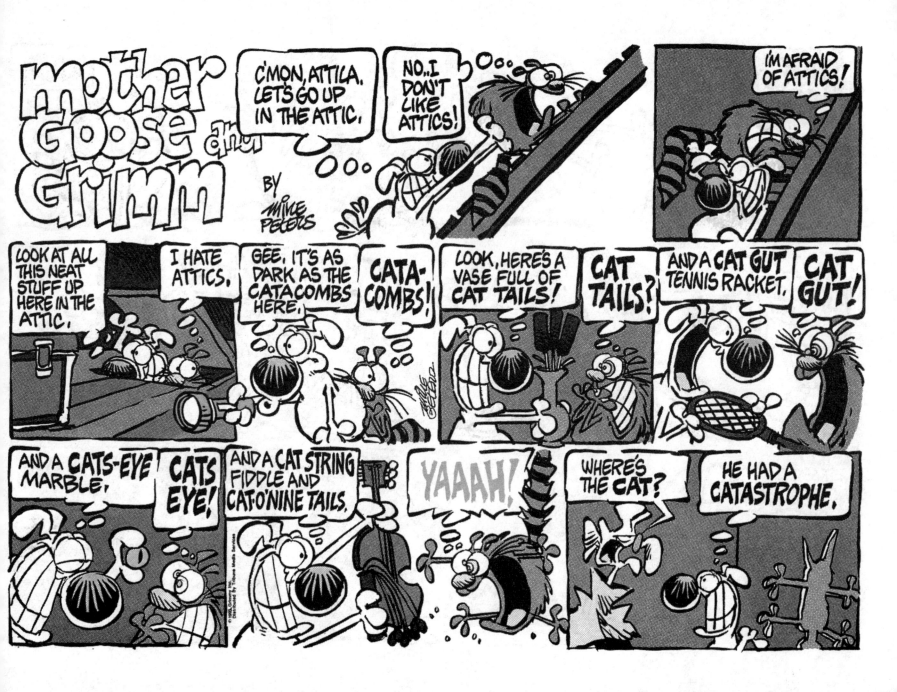

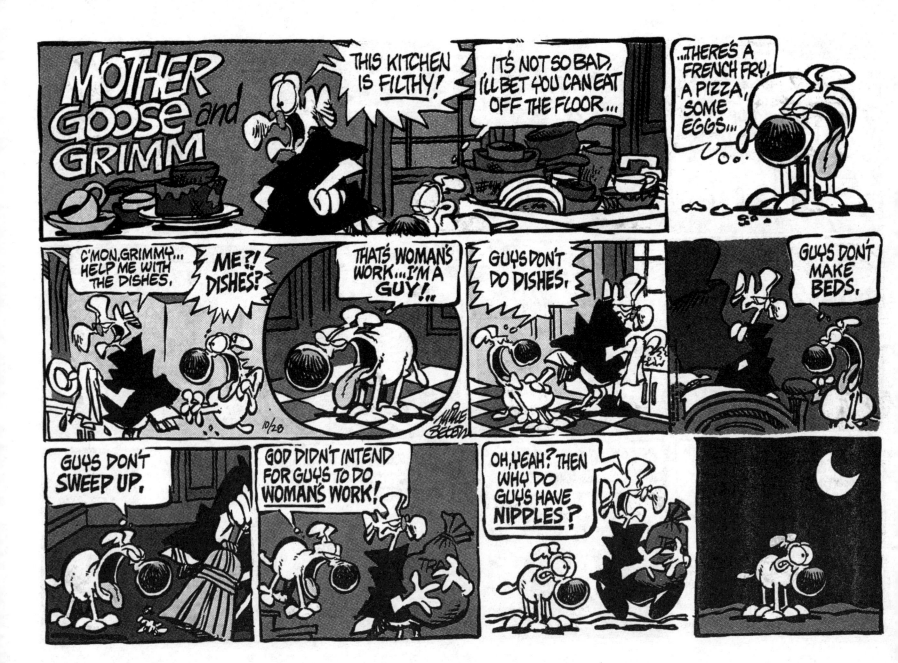

mother goose and Grimm

OH, NO, WE BROKE THE LAMP, MOTHER GOOSE WILL KILL US WHEN SHE FINDS OUT.

RELAX, ATTILA, SHE WON'T KILL US.... BELIEVE ME,

SHE WON'T DO ANYTHING TO US, I'VE GOT THE PERFECT EXCUSE.....

...THE CAT DID IT.

Mother Goose & GRIMM

BY Mike Peters

WHEN I WAS A PUP I HATED CLOSETS.

I ALWAYS THOUGHT THERE WAS A CLOSET MONSTER LIVING INSIDE...

HE HAD A THOUSAND FINGERS WITH SHARP, PRICKLY, LITTLE NAILS THAT WOULD GRAB YOU WHENEVER YOU RAN.

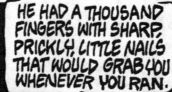

NOW THAT I'M OLDER I SEE HOW SILLY I WAS, THERE'S NOTHING TO BE AFRAID OF ABOUT A CLOSET.

WATCH... I'LL STAND IN THIS DARK CLOSET AND COUNT UP TO A HUNDRED.

ONE...TWO... THREE...FOUR...

© 1991 Grimmy Inc.
Distributed by Tribune Media Services

THE BLIND DATE OF
FRANKENSTEIN

AGNOSTIC FLEAS

MIME COURT

WHEN ROLY-POLYS CAMP OUT

12-24

SHE DENIES BEING A RUNAWAY, BUT I KNOW I SAW HER FACE ON A MILK CARTON.

POLICE

12-23

OOFWAY, ARKBAY, OWLHAY,

NOTHING DRIVES THEM UP THE WALL LIKE DOG LATIN....

12-26

THE SIGN SAID "TRASH CAN," SO I DID.

TRASH CAN

HEY, MAYBE THERE ARE SOME ADVANTAGES WHEN YOUR JAW LOCKS OPEN.

I'M REALLY WORRIED, ATTILA, NOBODY SEEMS TO CARE THAT MY JAW IS STUCK OPEN, EXCEPT YOU...

IT'S NICE TO KNOW THAT I HAVE ONE GOOD FRIEND WHO REALLY CARES...

"A FRIEND I CAN COUNT ON THAT WILL ALWAYS BE THERE, WILLING TO LISTEN, TO WHOM I CAN CONFIDE MY INNERMOST FEELINGS,

YOUR TONGUE IS COVERED WITH THOUSANDS OF REALLY GROSS-LOOKING BUMPS,

OH, NO... MY JAW'S STUCK OPEN AND MY MOUTH WON'T CLOSE AND THAT CUTE LITTLE POODLE KEEPS LOOKING AT ME.

I'D BETTER DO SOME-THING BEFORE SHE THINKS I'M WEIRD...

YAWN

...SO FAR, SO GOOD,

WHY CARTOONISTS DIDN'T LIVE LONG IN THE OLD WEST

THE LOIS AND CLARK EXPEDITION

THE GOOD, THE BAD AND
THE UGLY DUCKLING

JUNE 3, 1924, HARRY HOUDINI
LOCKS HIS KEYS INSIDE HIS BUICK

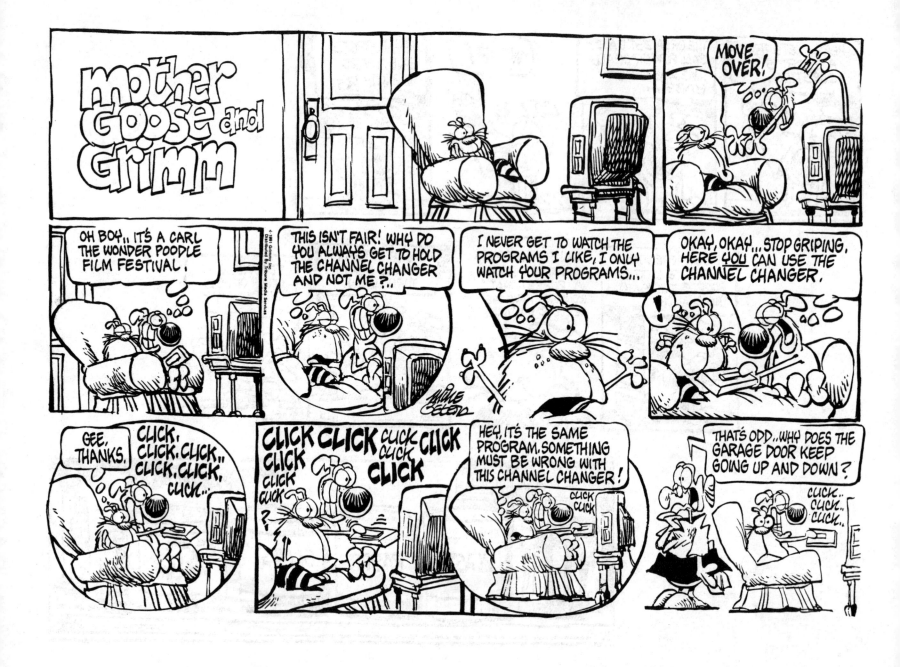

FLEA BARGAINING

PROBLEMS COMMON TO MARSUPIALS

GAG HACK..COUGH COUGH

DOGS HATE SECOND-HAND SMOKE.

EAT YOUR HEART OUT, JACQUES COUSTEAU....

HERE YOU GO, GRIMMY..YUMMY, DELICIOUS DOG FOOD...

HOW DOES SHE DO THAT WITH A STRAIGHT FACE?

Mother Goose & GRIMM

OH, ISN'T THAT CUTE? LOOK GRIMMY IS MOVING HIS LEG, HE MUST BE DREAMING.

DOGS HAVE DREAMS JUST LIKE THE REST OF US.

RIGHT NOW HE'S PROBABLY DREAMING THAT HE'S RUNNING ACROSS A FIELD....

..CHASING A SQUIRREL OR RABBIT OR SOME OTHER TYPICAL DOG THING.

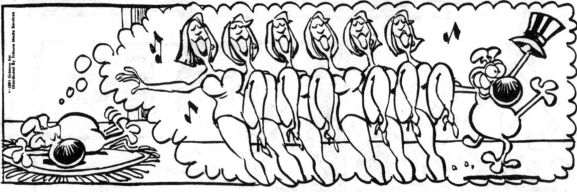

PRAIRIE DOGS WITH CHILI

1-27

HI, BEAUTIFUL, WHAT'S YOUR SIGN? LET'S HIT THE HAY.

BAR

THE CHEETAH IS THE FASTEST KNOWN LAND ANIMAL

2-5

HERE'S THE LITTLE FORMULA ONE, ALL SET FOR THE START OF THE BIG RACE.

...AS USUAL, HE'S IN THE POLL POSITION.

12-3

GRIMMY... YOU'VE GOT TO STOP THIS NONSENSE,

THIS ISN'T THE INDY 500, YOU'RE NOT A FORMULA ONE RACE CAR.

NOW...WHAT DO YOU WANT FOR DINNER?

PENSOIL.

12-4

FORMULA ONES ARE MADE FOR SPEED, THEY CAN GO FROM 0 TO 60 IN FIVE SECONDS...

THUD

...OR 60 TO 0 IN ONE SECOND.

12-5

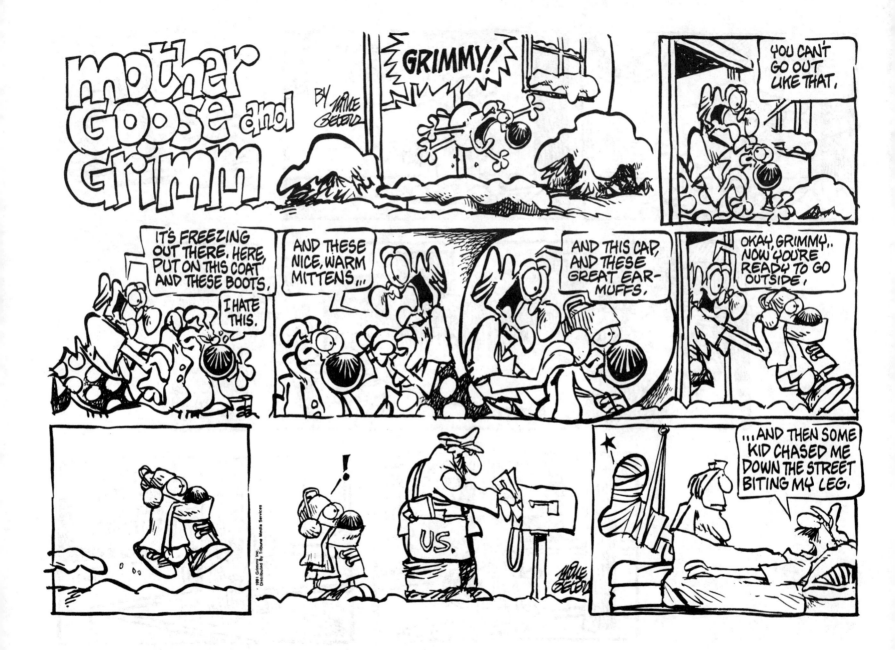

Row 1:

THIS ISN'T A CHRISTMAS TREE, ATTILA. THIS IS MY TREE. SHE GOT THIS TREE FOR ME...

12-13

...SHE BROUGHT THE TREE INSIDE SO I DON'T HAVE TO GO OUT IN THE SNOW, YA SEE?

...AND SHE PUT ON THOSE LIGHTS SO I COULD FIND THE TREE IN THE DARK, WHEN I'M WALKING AROUND,

GRIMM, WHAT'S THE WEATHER LIKE ON YOUR PLANET?

Row 2:

GRIMMY... THIS IS A CHRISTMAS TREE,

12-14

IT'S A SYMBOL OF GIVING AND SHARING THAT CHEERS THE HEARTS OF CHILDREN ALL OVER THE WORLD,

GRIMM, SURELY YOU'RE NOT THINKING OF DOING ANYTHING VILE OR DISGUSTING TO THIS WONDERFUL SYMBOL, ARE YOU?

YOU'VE GOT A PROBLEM WITH THAT?

Row 3:

SEE, GRIMMY...THIS CHRISTMAS TREE REPRESENTS EVERYTHING KIND AND GOOD AND LOVING DURING THIS GLORIOUS SEASON...

AURGHHH...

12-15

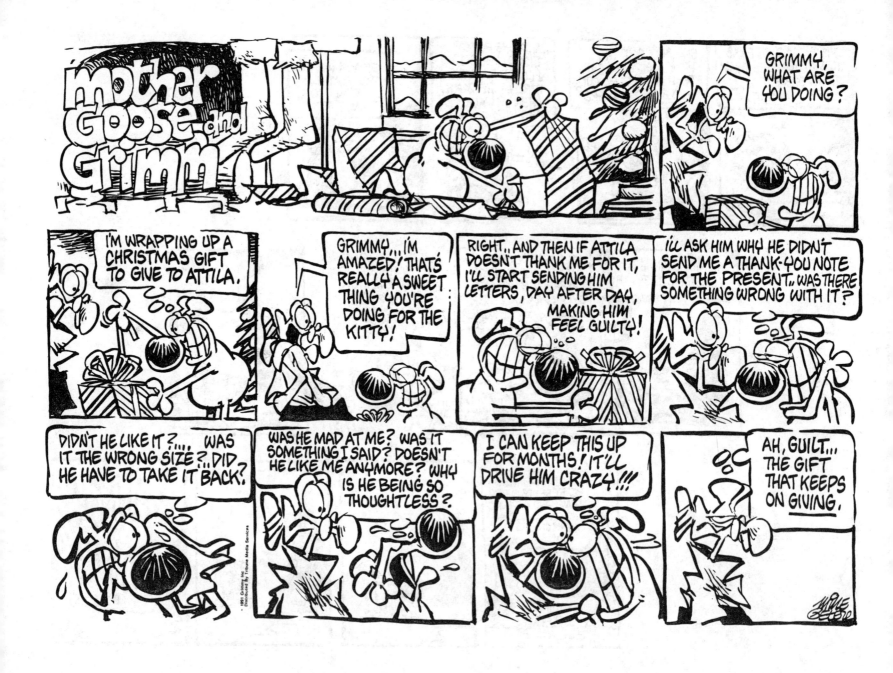

HANSEL AND GRETZKY

THE LONE RANGER AND TORONTO

PUNK ROCKERS

Heeeeeeeeeeeeeeeeere's

™